Fun with
Mo and Toots

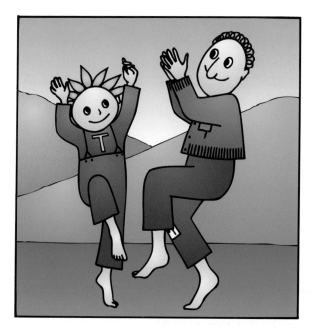

by Miriam Macdonald

Learning

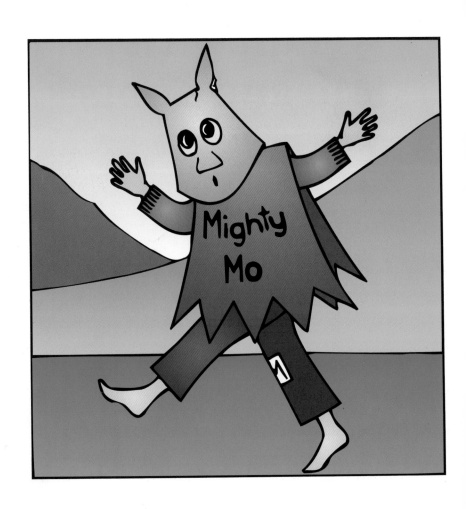

I like to dress up.

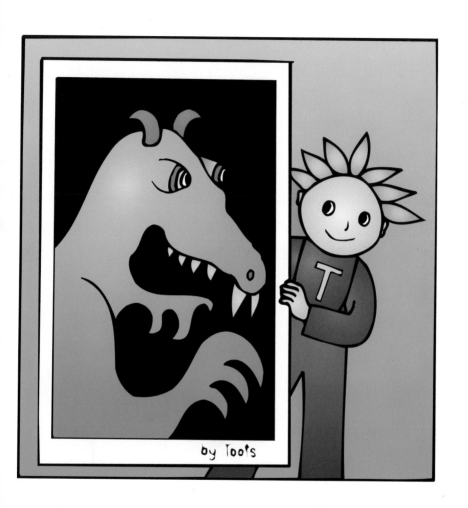

I like to draw monsters.

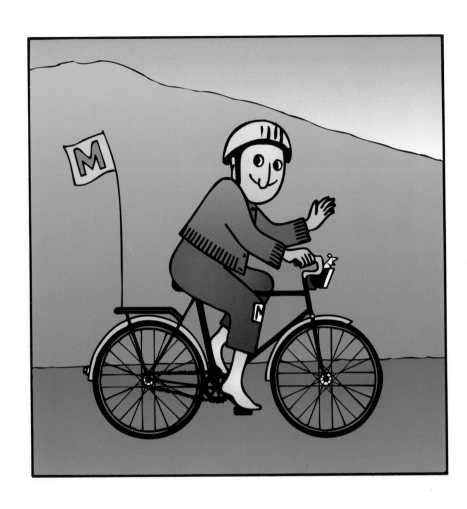

I like to ride my bike.

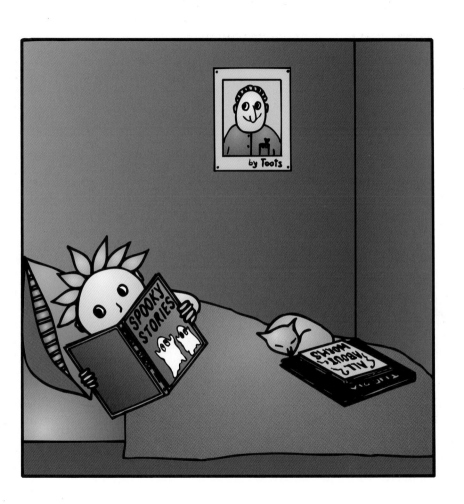

I like to read in bed.

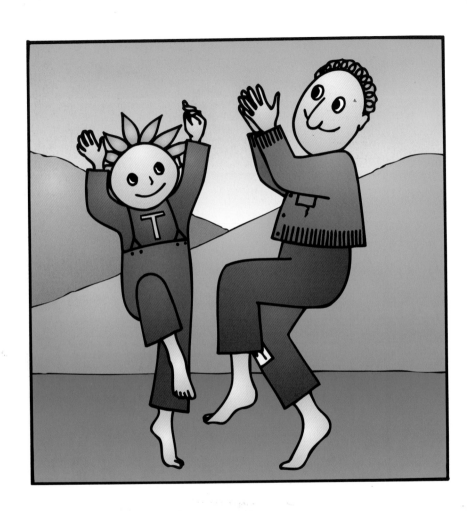

We like to dance.

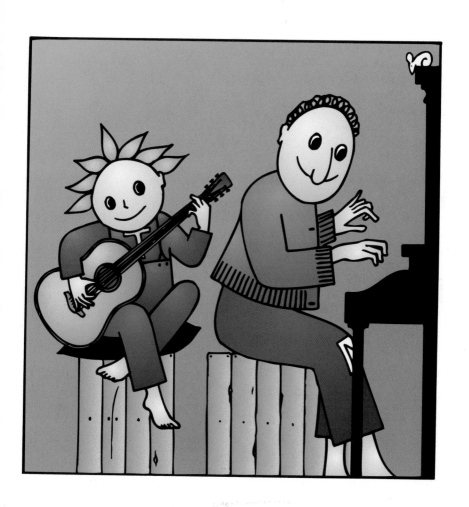

We like to make music.

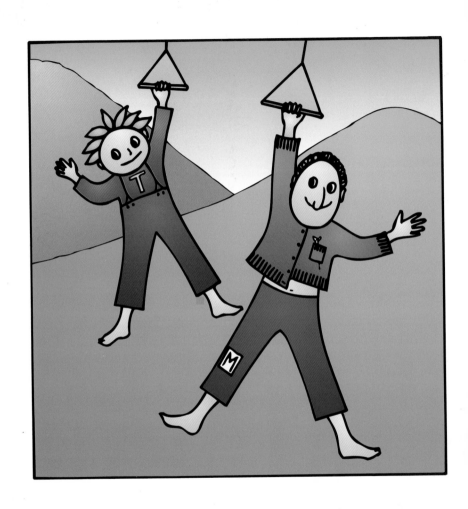

What do **you** like doing?